52 INTERACTIVE BIBLE STORIES

A COLLECTION OF OLD AND NEW TESTAMENT ACTION, ECHO, RHYTHM, AND SYLLABLE STORIES

Phyllis Vos Wezeman

The Pastoral Center

DEDICATION

To Ashley Marie Pallo... Celebrate the Story! (P.V.W.)

THANKS

To Active Learning Associates, Inc. and Educational Ministries, Inc.
for permission to include previously published stories in this collection.

ISBN 978-1-949628-03-6
Printed in the United States of America.
10 9 8 7 6 5 4 3 2 1   22 21 20 19 18

CONTENTS

CATEGORY INDEX

ACTION STORIES

Acts 2: Awaiting to Agape [Acts 2], 68
Creation: Day by Day [Genesis 1-2:3], 12
Footwashing: Served by the Savior [John 13:4-17], 59
Holy Week: Events and Emotions [Matthew 26:17-28:10; Mark 14:12-16:12; Luke 22:7-24:12; John 12:20-20:18], 62
Love: Just like Jesus [Matthew 22:37-39], 57
Moses: Plagues for Pharaoh [Exodus 5-11], 21
Pentecost: Sending the Spirit [Acts 2], 70
Peter: Feed the Flock [John 21:1-19], 67
Peter: Power in Prison [Acts 12:1-19], 74
Prayer: Ask for Answers [Luke 11:9-13], 49
Prodigal Son: Look at Love [Luke 15:11-32], 50
Psalm 150: One Spirit – One Story [Psalm 150], 32
Samuel: Prophet with a Purpose [1 Samuel 16:1-13], 26
Simeon and Anna: Dedicated and Devoted [Luke 2:21-40], 41
Sunday: Emotions of Easter [John 20:1-18], 65
Ten Commandments: Laws for Living [Exodus 20:1-21], 23
Unforgiving Servant: Actions and Attitudes [Matthew 18:23-25], 46
Zacchaeus: Called by Christ [Luke 19:1-10], 52

ECHO STORIES

Jesus' Transfiguration: Teach the Transformation [Luke 9:28-36], 55
Samson: Strength and Shame [Judges 13-16], 24
Sunday: Emotions of Easter [John 20:1-18], 65
Temple: Turn the Tables [Matthew 21:12-17; Mark 11:12-19; Luke 19:45-48], 56
Two Blind Men: Follow in Faith [Matthew 20:29-34], 47

RHYTHM STORIES

Abraham and Sarah: Strangers with a Surprise [Genesis 18:1-15; 21:1-7], 16
Adam and Eve: Creation and Consequences [Genesis 2:4b-3], 14
Daniel: Delivered from the Den [Daniel 6], 36
Disciples: Commissioned by Christ [Matthew 28:16-20; Mark 16:14-20; John 24:36-53], 64
Elijah: Protection and Provisions [1 Kings 17:1-7], 28
Elisha: Oil That's Overflowing [2 Kings 4:1-7], 29
Esther: Beauty and Bravery [Esther 1-10], 30
Holy Week: Day by Day [Matthew; Mark; Luke; John], 60
Isaac, Esau, and Jacob: Blessing a Brother [Genesis 27:1-29], 17
Isaiah: God's Promised Gift [Isaiah, Micah], 35
Jesus: Born in Bethlehem [Matthew 1:18-25; Luke 2:1-20], 39
Jesus: Risen to Reign [Matthew 28:1-9], 63
Lord's Prayer: Learn the Lessons [Matthew 6:9-13; Luke 11:1-14], 44
Lydia: Heart and Hospitality [Acts 16:11-15], 75
Moses: Burning Bush [Exodus 3; 4:1-17], 20
Moses: Saved to Serve [Exodus 2:2-10], 19
Noah: Built a Boat [Genesis 6:1-9:29], 15
Peter: Chosen and Called [Matthew 4:18-19; Mark 1:16-20; Luke 5:1-11], 43
Peter: Walks on Water [Matthew 14:22-33; Mark 6:45-52; John 6:15-21], 45
Ruth: Loyalty and Love [Ruth 1-4], 25
Saul to Paul: Converted to Christianity [Acts 9:1-31], 73
Ten Commandments: Laws for Living [Exodus 20:1-21], 23
Wise Men: Magi Seek Messiah [Matthew 2:1-12], 40
Woman at the Well: Living New Life [John 4:1-15, 25-30, 39-42], 53

SYLLABLE STORIES

Good Samaritan: Neighbor in Need [Luke 10:29-37], 48
John the Baptist: Messenger of the Messiah [Matthew 3:1-17; Mark 1:1-11; Luke 3:1-20; John 1:19-34], 42
Jonah: Learning a Lesson [Jonah 1-4], 37
Joseph: Rescued to Rule [Genesis 37:3-4, 12-36; Genesis 47:11-12], 18
Last to First: Places and Priorities [Mark 9:33-35], 54
Mary: Offered Her Ointment [John 12:1-8], 58
Psalm 100: Glorify Your God [Psalm 100], 31

SCRIPTURAL INDEX

OLD TESTAMENT

NEW TESTAMENT

INTRODUCTION

Get ready to have lots of fun with the children in your class! Believe me, they will love these brief excursions into the lives of biblical people. This collection tells stories using four methods, each of which involve the learner in the process and assure that the Bible story is meaningful as well as memorable. To make the best use of these activities, use the following directions for sharing each kind of story:

ACTION STORIES

Action stories include gestures and movements to interpret each line. This method involves learners in the process and assures that the Bible story is meaningful as well as memorable. To use an action story, have the group of listeners sit or stand facing the leader who tells the story and demonstrates all motions. Words to be repeated can be written out on newsprint or on a chalkboard, or can simply be emphasized with the voice so that the listeners understand the key word(s). The group or the leader may also improvise additional gestures and movements.

RHYTHM STORIES

The words of rhythm stories may be written on newsprint or on a chalkboard, or may simply be emphasized with the voice. To tell the story, have the participants sit or stand facing the leader. Begin by establishing the clapping pattern, one clap on the knees and one clap of the hands. Practice the beat several times. Say the first line of the story to this rhythm and tell the group to echo (or repeat) it back. Communicate the entire story in this manner. Maintain the established rhythm throughout.

ECHO STORIES

In an echo story the leader says a line and places special emphasis on the last phrase of each sentence, the capitalized word in the script. A gesture, such as raising a palm at the point where repetition is to begin, gives participants a clue to listen carefully for the words they are to repeat. Then the leader and the participants echo or recite these words together.

SYLLABLE STORIES

Share a Bible passage by using the two syllables in each line to tell the story. Establish the rhythm by slapping thighs once and snapping fingers of first one hand and then the other. Maintain this rhythmic pattern throughout the entire story. Say one syllable of the first line as thighs are slapped and the second syllable as fingers are snapped. The entire narrative is told in this quick, catchy manner.

HOW TO USE THE STORIES

While the contents of this collection are mainly intended for learners in a classroom, the material may be easily adapted for use by children, youth, and adults in small and large group settings. The stories are ideal for religious education classes, parochial school programs, vacation Bible school courses, confirmation sessions, intergenerational events, youth groups, retreat settings, family devotions, home schooling, and more. This collection will be welcomed by religious education directors, teachers, leaders, parents, and pastors.

In order to make the best use of this collection, let's consider a few ways that it will be helpful to the volunteer teacher leading a religion lesson in a parish setting.

Maybe you work from a prescribed curriculum or a purchased textbook to teach a class. The instructions are clear about what story to tell and the basic information to convey, but you are looking for some way to make the lesson more meaningful, memorable, and engaging. You want to involve the learners in the story so that they will appreciate the message for their lives. That's the point at which this book becomes an extremely helpful resource. The interactive stories can be used to open, enrich, expand, or conclude any lesson for five or ten minutes.

Or you may be a religious education teacher who is free to select the story you want to tell based on the season of the church year or the focus of a particular program. However, just knowing the focus for a lesson is not enough. Effective teachers know that a lesson has key elements that guide student learning from the introduction of an objective to a meaningful outcome. They accept responsibility for planning each lesson, much like an accomplished cook plans a balanced menu from appetizer to dessert. This book can help you include that key element of a successful lesson. Sift through the stories to find something catchy to introduce the lesson and the objective.

The beauty of this book is that no matter your teaching situation and no matter the lesson assigned, you can use and re-use the contents to find a fresh approach to telling the story—and, ultimately, to help your learners make it their story. Jesus used storytelling as his primary teaching tool. He improvised the lesson based on his listeners and their needs. While none of us can expect to teach like the Master, we can adopt a more flexible approach that allows creativity and innovation to guide our lesson preparation and presentation.

Have fun with these stories—I know you will.

—Phyllis Vos Wezeman

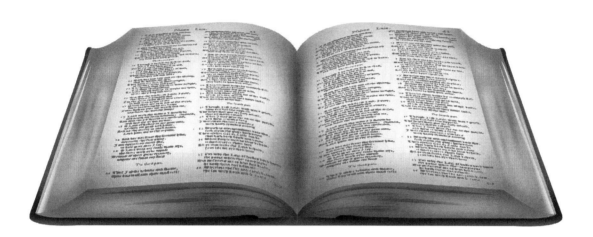

OLD TESTAMENT

CREATION *Day by Day*

Genesis 1-2:3 ♦ ACTION STORY

On Day One
[Hold up one finger]

God had fun!
[Smile]

Darkness - night!
[Close or cover eyes]

Daytime - light!
[Open or uncover eyes]

Then Day Two
[Hold up two fingers]

skies of blue.
[Cup hand over eyes and look up]

Now Day Three
[Raise three fingers]

earth came to be.
[Extend arms in front of body, making gesture of forming land]

Waters formed seas.
[Move arm up and down like waves]

Fruit filled trees.
[Extend arms overhead and move them like branches]

During Day Four
[Raise four fingers]

God made more!
[Open palm and extend arm from front to side of body]

Daytime - sun.
[Hold arms over head forming large circle]

Moon, just one,
[Form small circle with thumbs and fingertips]

shines at night.
[Point to sky]

Stars are bright!
[Hold up arms, open hands and move fingers in twinkling motion]

Day Five arrived!
[Raise five fingers]

Things came alive!
[Jump in place]

Birds in the air.
[Motion flying birds]

Fish everywhere.
[Motion swimming fish]

Came Day Six
[Hold up six fingers]

quite a mix!
[Roll arms in mixing motion]

Animals galore!
[Make movements of several different animals]

There was more!
[Hold up one hand in waiting or stop gesture]

People came too!
[Extend one hand from top to bottom of body]

Like me and you!
[Point to self and others]

Last - Day Seven.
[Hold up seven fingers]

God in heaven
[Point up]

blessed each one.
[Extend arm in gesture of blessing]

The job was done!
[Clap]

ADAM AND EVE
Creation and Consequences
Genesis 2:4b-3 ♦ RHYTHM STORY

When God made this great, big world,
He formed one special man
to care for the Creation.
It was part of God's plan.

Adam lived in the Garden of Eden
and tended God's creation there.
Lots of animals and trees and flowers,
but no people anywhere.

God could see that Adam was lonely,
and didn't want to live alone.
So God made another person
out of Adam's own rib bone.

God gave Adam and Eve the Garden
to be their very special home.
God said "Eat any fruit that you want,
just leave one certain tree alone."

A snake came to the woman
and tempted her to disobey.
"If you eat the fruit of this tree
you'll be wise as God today."

Eve ate and so did Adam,
although God had told them "No."
They tried to hide from their Maker,
but God found them and told them "Go!"

"Because you disobeyed me,
you must labor all your days.
Your life would have been much better
if you followed all God's ways."

NOAH *Built a Boat*

Genesis 6:1-9:29 ♦ RHYTHM STORY

There was a man named Noah,
he loved and served the Lord.
When God told him to build an ark,
poor Noah, he was floored.

He hammered and he pounded.
His neighbors laughed and jeered.
"There is no rain in sight," they said.
Noah's flipped his lid, they feared.

Noah followed God's instructions.
His family would be spared.
A flood would destroy the rest of the
   earth
because people had sinned and erred.

Noah gathered all his family,
and many animals, two by two.
They boarded the ark as God had
   planned.
It was a traveling zoo.

The rain came down for forty days.
Water covered all the land.
They stayed aboard for many months,
and were guided by God's hand.

When the water began receding
Noah wondered how he would know
when it was safe to leave the ark,
to pack his things and go.

Noah sent out a bird, the raven,
to see if dry land could be found.
But since the raven never returned,
it meant there was no dry ground.

Then Noah sent out a special bird,
a dove, so white and pure.
It returned to the ark with an olive
   branch.
Noah knew it was safe for sure.

The dove has become the symbol
of peace throughout the land.
The olive branch reminds us
that peace is part of God's plan.

Peacemaking Creatively through the Arts. Wezeman, Phyllis Vos. Prescott, AZ: Educational Ministries, 1990. Used by permission.

ABRAHAM AND SARAH
Strangers with a Surprise
Genesis 18:1-15; 21:1-7 ◆ RHYTHM STORY

As Abraham was sitting
outside his tent one day,
he saw some strangers walking
at a distance far away.

As the visitors approached him
he invited them to stay,
and he hurried to tell Sarah
to make supper right away.

While the messengers were eating
they conversed throughout the meal.
Then the purpose of their visit
they finally did reveal.

"We've been sent by God to tell you
the news that you will hear.
You will have a little baby,
a boy, this time next year."

Now Abraham and Sarah
were too old to have a child.
When they heard the angel's message
they thought the news was wild!

Sarah laughed and didn't believe it,
but the traveler said, "It's true!
God has promised you a nation.
There is nothing God can't do."

Of course, God kept His promise
and sent the couple their own son.
They named the baby Isaac,
God's gift, the special one.

ISAAC, ESAU, AND JACOB

Blessing a Brother

Genesis 27:1-29 ♦ RHYTHM STORY

When Isaac was an old man
he called his first-born son.
"Esau, you must have my blessing
since you are the oldest one."

"Go hunt for food and make me
my very favorite meal.
Then bring it to me promptly
and the promise I'll reveal."

Rebekah overheard her husband
and called her other son.
"Jacob, you will be the leader;
You are God's chosen one."

"Jacob, you must have the blessing
so here's what we will do.
Isaac's eyes are blind; he cannot see.
We will play a trick or two."

Rebekah made Isaac's favorite food,
and covered Jacob's skin with hair.
She found some clothes of Esau's
and gave them to Jacob to wear.

Jacob brought the food to Isaac
pretending to be the other twin.
"Your voice sounds very different.
Come, let me feel your skin."

After Isaac ate the dinner
he gave his blessing to this son:
"You will be the leader;
You will be the powerful one."

JOSEPH *Rescued to Rule*

Genesis 37:3-4, 12-36; 47:11-12 ◆ SYLLABLE STORY

Ja-cob's
fa-vorite
son was
Jo-seph.

Ja-cob
gave him
a gift
of a
bright-ly
color-ed
gar-ment.

This coat
was red,
and blue
and green.
It was
yel-low,
or-ange,
pur-ple,
char-treuse,
fuch-sia,
and more.

Jo-seph
wore it
proud-ly.

The gift
made his
other
broth-ers
jeal-ous.

One day
they stole
the coat
from Joe.

They sold
Jo-seph
to some
trad-ers.

But God
was with
Jo-seph.

God made
Jo-seph
rul-er
of all
E-gypt.

So Joe
saved his
fam-ily
dur-ing
a great
fa-mine.

Jo-seph's
broth-ers
were so
sor-ry
and he
for-gave
them all.

God helps
those who
love and
trust Him.

MOSES *Saved to Serve*

Exodus 2:2-10 ♦ RHYTHM STORY

When Moses was a baby
Egypt's Pharaoh had a wicked plan:
to kill the first male newborns
of the Israelites throughout his land.

Moses' mother wove a basket.
She laid her precious son inside.
She placed it in the river
and in tall grass the baby could hide.

While Moses' sister Miriam
watched her brother in the Nile,
she saw Pharaoh's daughter coming
and her heart began to smile.

When the princess found the baby
she adopted him as her son.
God had special plans for Moses.
Moses was God's chosen one.

God called Moses to lead His people
as they struggled for many years.
Moses' journey lasted a lifetime
and was filled with challenges and fears.

God delivered the people of Israel.
He provided for them night and day.
We can trust in God to guide us
and be with us in every way.

MOSES *Burning Bush*

Exodus 3; 4:1-17 ♦ RHYTHM STORY

While Moses watched the sheep one day
he saw a very strange sight.
A bush was burning brightly;
It was on fire alright!

As Moses stepped a little closer
a voice spoke some special words:
"Moses, you will be Israel's leader."
This message from God was heard.

Moses said he didn't speak well.
and he wouldn't know what to do.
God said, "Aaron can be your helper.
Trust me. I will be with you."

"You must lead my people safely
from their slavery in Pharaoh's land.
I will guide you and protect you.
This is all part of God's plan."

Moses told the king:
there'll be awful things!

"Let my people go!"
[Shake head yes]
Pharaoh still said "no!"
[Shake head no]

Water turned to blood
Punishment from God.

"Let my people go!"
[Shake head yes]
Pharaoh still said "no!"
[Shake head no]

Frogs hopped everywhere.
Even in the air!

"Let my people go!"
[Shake head yes]
Pharaoh still said "no!"
[Shake head no]

Gnats swarmed all the land.
That's what God had planned.

"Let my people go!"
[Shake head yes]
Pharaoh still said "no!"
[Shake head no]

Flies were number four.
Could there still be more?

"Let my people go!"
[Shake head yes]
Pharaoh still said "no!"
[Shake head no]

Animals got sick.
Make them better quick!

"Let my people go!"
[Shake head yes]
Pharaoh still said "no!"
[Shake head no]

Sores made people sick.
Still another trick.

"Let my people go!"
    [Shake head yes]
Pharaoh still said "no!"
    [Shake head no]

Hail ruined every crop.
Please just make it stop.

"Let my people go!"
    [Shake head yes]
Pharaoh still said "no!"
    [Shake head no]

Locust here and there.
They were everywhere.

"Let my people go!"
    [Shake head yes]
Pharaoh still said "no!"
    [Shake head no]

Darkness day and night!
Give us back the light.

"Let my people go!"
    [Shake head yes]
Pharaoh still said "no!"
    [Shake head no]

Death took first-born sons
Each and every one!

Pharaoh didn't say "no!"
    [Shake head no]
Take your folks and "go!"
    [Shake head yes]

TEN COMMANDMENTS
Laws for Living
Exodus 20:1-21 ♦ ACTION STORY

Commandment number one
is simple to recall:
There is only one God
Jehovah, Lord of all.
    [Raise one finger]

Commandment number two
has good advice for you.
Do not serve any idols
There's just one God that's true.
    [Raise two fingers]

God's name is very special
hold it in high regard.
That's commandment number three.
That isn't very hard.
    [Raise three fingers]

Sunday is a special day.
Do not work, but rest.
The fourth commandment tells us
that Sunday is the best.
    [Raise four fingers]

Your father and your mother
are gifts from God to you.
Commandment number five says
honor them in all you do.
    [Raise five fingers]

Do not murder is number six
the commandment after five.
The special creatures God has made
must all be kept alive.
    [Raise six fingers]

Be faithful to the one you love
is seven's guide for life.
This is a good commandment
for a husband and a wife.
    [Raise seven fingers]

Commandment eight says do not take
what doesn't belong to you.
By keeping this commandment
you praise God in all you do.
    [Raise eight fingers]

Don't bear false witness, number nine
means in everything you do
you must tell the truth about others.
It is God's law for you.
    [Raise nine fingers]

There may be things that others have
that you'd like to have too.
Number ten says do not covet.
This is God's guide for you.
    [Raise ten fingers]

SAMSON *Strength and Shame*

Judges 13-16 ◆ ECHO STORY

Samson's special gift from God was **STRENGTH**. (STRENGTH)

When he fought the lion he was **SAVED**. (SAVED)

People tried to learn about the **SOURCE**. (SOURCE)

He did mighty acts 'cause he was **STRONG**. (STRONG)

Delilah tried to figure out his **SECRET**. (SECRET)

Finally Samson told her to use **SCISSORS**. (SCISSORS)

Then she took his hair and made a **SNIP**. (SNIP)

Samson lost his strength and then came **SHAME**. (SHAME)

Since he didn't trust God he had to **SUFFER**. (SUFFER)

Once again he prayed that he might **SERVE**. (SERVE)

And God gave him back some of his **STRENGTH**. (STRENGTH)

Samson pulled a building and it **SHATTERED**. (SHATTERED)

All the wicked folks inside were **SMASHED**. (SMASHED)

Samson's strength showed that God was **SUPREME**. (SUPREME)

RUTH *Loyalty and Love*
Ruth 1-4 ◆ RHYTHM STORY

Elimelech lived in Bethlehem
with Naomi, his faithful wife.
When a famine swept across the land,
their home was filled with strife.

With their sons Mahlon and Chilion
they decided to move away.
They went to the land of Moab,
found food, and decided to stay.

While in Moab the two boys married.
Orpah and Ruth became their brides.
But then a sad thing happened:
Naomi's husband and two sons died.

When there was food in the land of Judah
Naomi said "I must return to my home."
Orpah left and went back to her family
but Ruth wouldn't leave Naomi alone.

"Entreat me not to leave you.
Where you go, I'll go too.
Your God will be my own God."
This is what Ruth wanted to do.

Ruth went to the field of Boaz.
She gleaned grain that was left behind.
Boaz gave Ruth an extra measure.
To the faithful woman he was kind.

Later Ruth and Boaz married.
God sent them a baby son.
Obed became the father of Jesse,
and heir of Jesus, God's holy one.

SAMUEL *Prophet with a Purpose*

1 Samuel 16:1-3 ♦ ACTION STORY

God told Samuel:
[Cup hands to mouth]

"Go to the house of Jesse;
[Walk in place]

Anoint the next King of Israel."
[Make pouring motion]

Jesse had eight sons.
[Hold up eight fingers]

One by one they came to meet Samuel.
[Shake hands]

Son number one was the oldest.
[Hold up one finger]

Son number two was very tall.
[Hold up two fingers]

Son number three was handsome.
[Hold up three fingers]

Son number four was strong.
[Hold up four fingers]

Son number five was a hard worker.
[Hold up five fingers]

Son number six was well liked.
[Hold up six fingers]

Son number seven was well dressed.
[Hold up seven fingers]

Any of them would make a good king!
[Shake head yes]

Each time God told Samuel "No."
[Shake head no]

"This is not the one I have chosen."
[Hold up hand and gesture stop]

Do not look at the way a person looks on the outside.
[Point to outside of body]

Look at the way a person looks on the inside.
[Point to heart]

▷

Jesse had one more son.
   [Hold up one finger]

David was watching the sheep.
   [Hold one hand over eyes]

Jesse sent for David.
   [Motion come]

Son number eight, young David, did not look like a king.
   [Hold up eight fingers]

But God said, "This is the one I have chosen."
   [Shake head yes]

God looks on the inside - at a person's heart.
   [Point to heart]

Samuel anointed David to be the next king of Israel.
   [Make pouring motion over head]

ELIJAH *Protection and Provisions*

1 Kings 17:1-7 ♦ RHYTHM STORY

Elijah of Tishbee in Galilee
brought God's message to Ahab, the King.
"There will be no dew or rainfall,
because you've done a terrible thing."

After Elijah brought the King the warning
God told the prophet to go and hide.
Elijah went to the brook called Cherith
with God, the Protector, at his side.

Then the brook became his water.
Meat and bread came every day.
It was brought to him by ravens.
God took care of him in every way.

ELISHA *Oil That's Overflowing*

2 Kings 4:1-7 ♦ RHYTHM STORY

Elisha was a prophet,
a man who spoke the Word.
As he traveled 'round the country
the voice of God was heard.

Elisha met a woman
whose husband had just died.
"Elisha, will you help me?"
The upset lady cried.

"I have no funds to pay my bills.
My child will be sold as a slave.
I am trusting God to help us
though our plight looks very grave."

"We only have one jug of oil.
That will not get us very far."
Elisha said, "Go ask your neighbors
to borrow every available jar."

"Just keep pouring from your bottle
until the jars all overflow.
When you go and sell the oil
you'll have money then, I know."

The woman listened to Elisha
and she was blessed indeed.
Since she trusted God to help her
God met her every need.

ESTHER *Beauty and Bravery*

Esther 1-10 ◆ RHYTHM STORY

When Xerxes was king of Persia
he held a banquet for all around.
There were many months of feasting;
It was the biggest party in town.

To please the men at the party
he called his wife, Queen Vashti, to dance.
But he banned her from the kingdom
when she said "There's not a chance!"

The king was sad and lonely
so his officials had a plan.
"We'll find the most beautiful woman
to be queen for this powerful man."

When Mordecai learned of the contest
he brought his relative Esther to be
the queen of all of Persia.
The king said, "She pleases me!"

An evil man named Haman
had a very wicked plan:
"Let's kill all the Jews in Persia.
We don't want them in our land."

When Mordecai got this message
he tore his clothes and began to cry.
Then he begged and pleaded with Esther:
"Tell the king or we all will die."

Esther was a Jew, but kept it secret
now her life was on the line.
She asked Xerxes and Haman to a
    banquet.
They said, "Yes! We'll come and dine!"

At the banquet Esther asked a favor
"Come to dinner again tomorrow night."
She told the king of the plot to kill her
    people
and asked him to save her from this
    plight.

Now the king was filled with anger.
Who would think of such a wicked plan?
Esther pointed her finger at Haman:
"Your high official is the evil man."

Then Haman was hanged on the gallows
that he had built to kill a Jew.
Mordecai was made the new prime
    minister.
In Persian power he became number two.

God spared the lives of the Jewish people.
Esther and Mordecai led the way.
Jews still celebrate the Feast of Purim
to commemorate this happy day.

PSALM 100 *Glorify Your God*

Psalm 100 ◆ SYLLABLE STORY

Make a
joy-ful
noise all
peo-ple.

Serve the
Lord with
glad-ness.

Come to
God with
sing-ing.

Know that
the Lord
is God.

God made
you. You
are His.

Give thanks
and bless
God's name.

God's love
en-dures
for-ever.

PSALM 150
One Spirit, One Story
Psalm 150 ◆ ACTION STORY

AFRICA—SHAKERS

**African believers raise a shaker
to offer praise to God, their maker!**
   *[Demonstrate the shakers or mime the
   action of playing them]*

Refrain

Same story!
   *[Hold hands in front of body to form the
   shape of a book]*

Different sound!
   [Cup hand to ear]

One Spirit!
   *[Raise arms overhead and hold up one
   finger on each hand]*

World around!
   *[Raise arms overhead to form a circle or
   extend arms at sides]*

ASIA—GONG

**God's people in Asia use a gong
to celebrate that they belong!**
   *[Demonstrate the gong or mime the action
   of striking the instrument]*

Refrain

Same story!
   *[Hold hands in front of body to form the
   shape of a book]*

Different sound!
   [Cup hand to ear]

One Spirit!
   *[Raise arms overhead and hold up one
   finger on each hand]*

World around!
   *[Raise arms overhead to form a circle or
   extend arms at sides]*

AUSTRALIA—DIDGERY DOO

A didgery doo sounds out praise and wonder
for Australian worshipers who sing Down Under!
[Demonstrate the didgery doo or mime the action of playing it]

Refrain

Same story!
[Hold hands in front of body to form the shape of a book]

Different sound!
[Cup hand to ear]

One Spirit!
[Raise arms overhead and hold up one finger on each hand]

World around!
[Raise arms overhead to form a circle or extend arms at sides]

EUROPE—HORN

In Europe to sound of flute and horn
disciples praise God, they've been re-born!
[Demonstrate the horn or mime the action of playing it]

Refrain

Same story!
[Hold hands in front of body to form the shape of a book]

Different sound!
[Cup hand to ear]

One Spirit!
[Raise arms overhead and hold up one finger on each hand]

World around!
[Raise arms overhead to form a circle or extend arms at sides]

NORTH AMERICA—DRUM

North American Christians beat a drum and pray as one "God's Kingdom come!"
[Demonstrate the drum or mime the action of playing it]

Refrain

Same story!
[Hold hands in front of body to form the shape of a book]

Different sound!
[Cup hand to ear]

One Spirit!
[Raise arms overhead and hold up one finger on each hand]

World around!
[Raise arms overhead to form a circle or extend arms at sides]

SOUTH AMERICA—MANDOLIN

A mandolin is South America's sound for Jesus' followers in village and town.
[Demonstrate the mandolin or mime the action of playing it]

Refrain

Same story!
[Hold hands in front of body to form the shape of a book]

Different sound!
[Cup hand to ear]

One Spirit!
[Raise arms overhead and hold up one finger on each hand]

World around!
[Raise arms overhead to form a circle or extend arms at sides]

ISAIAH *God's Promised Gift*

Isaiah, Micah ◆ RHYTHM STORY

Long ago God's prophets told us
to get ready for the Savior.
Stop your sinful way of living.
Make a change in your behavior.

Isaiah said that God's own Son
would be the sacrificial lamb.
His blood would cover all our sin.
God will accept me as I am.

Isaiah offered many names
that told us who this child would be:
Wonderful Counselor, Mighty God,
The Prince of Peace for you and me.

Micah said that a tiny town
would be the site of Jesus' birth.
In Bethlehem one holy night
would come the Savior of the earth.

This King would be from David's line,
a ruler from the royal throne.
The One God promised long ago:
Emmanuel—we're not alone.

Before God's great Messiah came
the prophets praised His holy name.
God's faithfulness and constant love
from age to age remains the same.

DANIEL *Delivered from the Den*

Daniel 6 ♦ RHYTHM STORY

During the reign of King Darius
the ruler made a new decree:
"All prayers and praise for thirty days
must be offered unto me."

Now Daniel was devoted
to Israel's God alone.
He would not bow down to worship
a king on an earthly throne.

Evil men opposing Daniel
saw him praying in his room.
So they went to tell the king to bring
poor Daniel to his doom!

"Punish him for disobeying,"
said the wicked, nasty men.
So poor unsuspecting Daniel
was thrown in the lion's den.

"May the God you trust be with you.
May He guard you from all ill."
Daniel told the King with assurance,
"I know that Jehovah will."

At daybreak the sad king hurried
to check on poor Daniel's plight.
But since Daniel put his trust in God
no harm came to him that night.

So Daniel was delivered
from the ferocious lion's den.
The Lord had been victorious!
God had triumphed once again!

"Jo-nah,
I want
you to
go to
Nine-vah."

"Tell the
peo-ple
there that
they must
re-pent!"

Jo-nah
got on
a ship
to run
from God.

There was
a great
storm and
peo-ple
were afraid.

The crew
cast lots
to see
who was
at fault.

They threw
Jo-nah
over-board
in-to
the sea.

He lived
in-side
a big
fish for
three days.

Jo-nah
prayed to
God and
said he'd
done wrong.

Then the
big fish
spit him
on-to
dry ground.

Jo-nah
preached and
told folks
to love
his God.

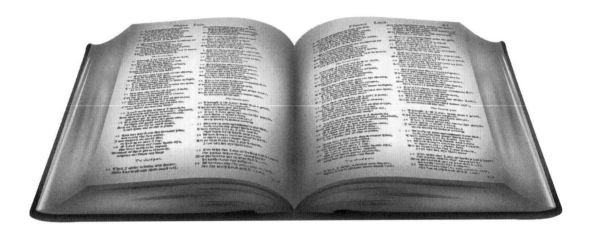

NEW TESTAMENT

JESUS *Born in Bethlehem*

Matthew 1:18-25; Luke 2:1-20 ◆ RHYTHM STORY

Mary and Joseph went on a journey
to a city far away.
They were on their way to Bethlehem,
their taxes to Caesar to pay.

The city was crowded and busy.
There was no place for them to stay.
The innkeeper showed them a stable.
They could rest on the straw and the hay.

During the night something happened.
Mary had a baby boy:
the Son of God and the Son of Man.
Her heart was filled with joy.

While shepherds watched their flocks
that night
the sky was filled with light.
An angel host appeared to them.
It was a glorious sight.

The angel told the Good News
of the blessed Savior's birth.
They took their flocks and went to see
the Lord of all the earth.

They entered the stable with reverence
to honor the newborn King.
We still praise the Christ of Christmas
as we worship and pray and sing.

Advent Alphabet. Wezeman, Phyllis Vos and Jude Dennis Fournier. Prescott, AZ: Educational Ministries, Inc., 1989. Used by permission.

THE WISE MEN *Magi Seek Messiah*

Matthew 2:1-12 ♦ RHYTHM STORY

Three wise men went on a journey.
They had to travel very far.
They passed through deserts and
     mountains,
and were guided by God's star.

They arrived at the palace of Herod.
He was ruler of the land.
They asked where to find the baby.
It was all part of God's plan.

Herod called his chief priests together
to determine where the babe might be.
Bethlehem was the answer they gave him.
The wise men would go and see.

When the magi left King Herod
the star shone very bright.
It led them to the Savior.
It was a holy night.

The wise men gave their treasures
to honor the newborn king.
All earth and heaven would join them:
Jesus' glory and greatness to sing.

Symbols of the Season: Exciting Epiphany Experiences. Wezeman, Phyllis Vos and Jude Dennis Fournier. Prescott, AZ: Educational Ministries, Inc., 1989. Used by permission.

SIMEON AND ANNA
Dedicated and Devoted
Luke 2:21-40 ♦ RHYTHM STORY

Eight days after Jesus' birth
Mary and Joseph brought their son
to the temple in Jerusalem
to present the Holy One.

A righteous man named Simeon
waited for the Savior's birth.
He trusted God to send the one
Who would bring peace to all the earth.

When Simeon saw the Christ Child
he held him close and praised:
"My eyes have seen salvation."
Mary and Joseph were amazed.

Eighty-four-year-old Anna
trusted God enough to know
the Savior of the world had come.
God's glory He would show.

Mary and Joseph left the temple
and the child grew and grew.
He was the Savior of the world
just as Simeon and Anna knew.

JOHN THE BAPTIST
Messenger of the Messiah

John 1:19-34; Matthew 3:1-17; Mark 1:1-11; Luke 3:1-20 ♦
SYLLABLE STORY

"Pre-pare
the way
for the
Mes-siah,"
John the
Bap-tist
told the
peo-ple.

"The one
for whom
you've been
wait-ing
is here!"

"Re-pent,
be-lieve,
and be
bap-tized,"
cried John
as he
trav-eled
through-out
the land.

John once
bap-tized
Je-sus
in the
Jor-dan
Riv-er.

God the
Fa-ther
sent the
Spir-it
in the
form of
a dove.
And God
said, "This
is my
be-loved
Son in
Whom I
am well
pleas-ed."

PETER *Chosen and Called*

Matthew 4:18-19; Mark 1:16-20; Luke 5:1-11 ♦
RHYTHM STORY

On the shore of Lake Gennesaret
Jesus stood to preach God's word.
When the people crowded closer
His voice could not be heard.

A boat that belonged to Peter
was right within his reach.
He took it into the water
and he sat in it to teach.

When Jesus finished speaking
He told Peter what to do:
"Push out the boat; let down the nets.
There will be a catch for you."

Peter and the other partners
had fished throughout the night.
They hadn't caught a single thing.
There were no fish in sight.

Peter told Jesus how hard they'd labored.
Yet, he cast the nets in deep.
Soon they were filled to almost breaking;
There were so many fish to keep.

When Peter saw Jesus' power
he fell on his knees and cried:
"Lord, I am just a sinner,
I'm not worthy to be at your side."

Jesus had a surprising answer:
"Peter, come and follow me.
We'll be catching people instead of fish.
My disciple you will be."

THE LORD'S PRAYER
Learn the Lessons

Matthew 6:9-13; Luke 11:1-14 ◆ RHYTHM STORY

"Our Father in heaven"
are the words that we say
as we begin the prayer
Jesus taught us to pray.

Hallowed be Thy name—
God's great. It's true.
Let our words and our deeds
honor God in all we do.

"Thy kingdom come" seems simple!
These are easy words to say.
They mean we must do God's will
each and every day.

Thy will be done on earth
as it is in heaven, too.
May others know God's love
through all the things we do.

Our daily bread's a gift
that shows God's loving care.
May we always want to share
with God's people everywhere.

"Forgive our sins" we pray
as we forgive each other
Let's show God's love to all—
each sister and each brother.

Temptation—lead us from it.
Keep us from evil, too.
May our life be an example
of praise in all we do.

The kingdom and the power
and all the glory, too
Are given unto God—
unto the Lord it's due.

PETER *Walks on Water*

Matthew 14:22-33; Mark 6:45-52; John 6:15-21 ♦
RHYTHM STORY

Simon was a fisherman,
a loud, outspoken guy.
But he left his net, his boat, his fish
when Jesus happened by.

"Come follow me," said Jesus.
"I'll even change your name."
"You'll be my rock of faith," he said.
Peter never was the same.

He learned to fish for people.
He stayed close by Jesus' side.
"My faith in you," said Peter
"can never be denied."

"I can even walk on water.
Watch and tell me what you think!"
But he took his eyes off Jesus.
"Master help me or I'll sink!"

No Peter wasn't perfect.
He was just like you and me.
But Jesus looked past Peter's faults
and saw who he could be.

So when we follow Jesus
though we might not change our name,
we will learn to fish for people,
and we'll never be the same.

"Peter Walks on Water." *Pilgrimage: Seeking the Kingdom of God*. Wezeman, Phyllis Vos, Anna L. Liechty, and Judith Harris Chase. Mishawaka, IN: Active Learning Associates, Inc., 1998.

THE UNFORGIVING SERVANT
Actions and Attitudes
Matthew 18:23-25 ♦ ACTION STORY

One day the King called to the palace the people who owed him money.
"You owe!"
 [Point away from self]

"It's time for you to repay your debts!"
"Oh no!"
 [Shake head no]

A certain slave owed the King 10,000 talents.
Big debt!
 [Extend arms at sides]

But the man said he couldn't give it back.
"Not yet!"
 [Shrug shoulders]

So the debtor pleaded for mercy!
"Let me live!"
 [Fold hands and beg]

In generosity, the king cancelled the debt.
"I forgive!"
 [Extend one arm at side]

Immediately, the forgiven man went to find a person who owed him a few dollars.
Oh, wow!
 [Place hand over eyes and look around]

The forgiven servant told his debtor to give him the money.
"Pay now!"
 [Hold out hand]

When the poor man said he couldn't pay,
"No money!"
 [Gesture empty pockets]

The forgiven servant had him thrown in prison.
Not funny!
 [Sad face]

But the prison guards didn't think this was right.
Not fair!
 [Scratch head]

So they went to tell the King
"Beware!"
 [Walk in place]

Then the King called the servant he had forgiven.
"Lost trust!"
 [Motion come here]

And told him that his debt was due immediately.
"You must!"
 [Pound fist]

Because God forgives us
Thank you!
 [Point up]

We must forgive each other!
Me too!
 [Point to self]

TWO BLIND MEN *Follow in Faith*

Matthew 20:29-34 ♦ ECHO STORY

LEADER As Jesus and his friends were leaving Jericho, the crowd said: "Let's follow Jesus!"

ALL "Let's follow Jesus!" *[whisper]*
"Let's follow Jesus!" *[speak]*
"Let's follow Jesus!" *[shout]*

LEADER Two blind men sitting by the side of the road, pleaded: "Jesus, have mercy on us!"

ALL "Jesus, have mercy on us!" *[whisper]*
"Jesus, have mercy on us!" *[speak]*
"Jesus, have mercy on us!" *[shout]*

LEADER The crowd told the blind men: "Be Quiet!"

ALL "Be quiet!" *[whisper]*
"Be quiet!" *[speak]*
"Be quiet!" *[shout]*

LEADER The blind men shouted: "Jesus, have mercy on us!"

ALL "Jesus, have mercy on us!" *[whisper]*
"Jesus, have mercy on us!" *[speak]*
"Jesus, have mercy on us!" *[shout]*

LEADER Jesus stopped and listened to the blind men. He asked: "What do you want me to do for you?"

ALL "What do you want me to do for you?" *[whisper]*
"What do you want me to do for you?" *[speak]*
"What do you want me to do for you?" *[shout]*

LEADER The blind men answered: "Jesus, let our eyes be opened."

ALL "Jesus, let our eyes be opened." *[whisper]*
"Jesus, let our eyes be opened." *[speak]*
"Jesus, let our eyes be opened." *[shout]*

LEADER Jesus touched their eyes and the blind men exclaimed: "We can see! Let's follow Jesus!"

ALL "We can see! Let's follow Jesus!" *[whisper]*
"We can see! Let's follow Jesus!" *[speak]*
"We can see! Let's follow Jesus!" *[shout]*

THE GOOD SAMARITAN
Neighbor in Need

Luke 10:29-37 ♦ SYLLABLE STORY

When the
law-yer
asked "Who
is my
neigh-bor?"
Je-sus
an-swered:

"One day
a man
walk-ing
down the
road to
Jer-icho
was robbed
and beaten
and left
for dead.

A priest
crossed the
street to
a-void
the man.

And, so
did a
Le-vite.

When a
Sa-mar
i-tan
passed by
he stopped
to help
the man.

Then he
took the
man to
an inn
and paid
for his
treat-ment.

Who was
the best
neigh-bor?"

PRAYER *Ask for Answers*

Luke 11:9-13 ◆ ACTION STORY

The disciples wanted to learn to pray.
[Hold up praying hands]

But prayer is more than the words we say.
[Cup hands to mouth]

Jesus said we must ask each day
[Hold up hand like asking a question]

and keep on asking when we pray.
[Support arm with other hand while continuing to ask]

In order to know how to live each day,
[Shrug shoulders; extend arms at sides]

Jesus said we must seek God's way
[Put one hand above eyes and look left and right]

The door of God's love isn't locked away.
[Cross hands over chest]

We can knock and receive today
[Mime knocking on a door]

the gift of God's Spirit. Hip! Hip! Hooray!
[Open arms upward, then cheer!]

THE PRODIGAL SON *Look at Love*

Luke 15:11-32 ♦ ACTION STORY

There once was a father who had two sons.
One liked to work; one liked to have fun.
The older son worked hard all day,
while the younger son just liked to play.
   [Raise hands and extend index fingers
   upward to represent each son]

The younger son thought of a plan.
He thought that he was now a man.
He asked his father
   for his share of the money.
He left for a place
   he thought would be sunny.
   [Wave good-bye]

When he got there,
   he made lots of friends,
but would they be true
   when the money ends?
He partied and played
   from morning till night.
It wasn't too long until money was tight.
   [Make motion of emptying pockets]

He was starving and lonely
   and tired of the work.
He looked at himself and said,
   "What a jerk!"
"Where are my friends
   when I need them so badly?
When I had money,
   they hung around gladly!"
   [Raise hand to forehead and look around]

"My father's workers eat better than I,"
he said with sadness and a great big sigh.
"I will go back
   and have faith he's forgiving.
This is no way for me to be living."
   [Raise hands and cross fingers]

"My father loved me more than I knew.
Now I know the right thing to do.
I don't deserve to be a son,
but I can help with the work to be done."
   [Fold hands in prayerful gesture]

He started home that very day,
but when he still was far away,
his father saw him and shouted with glee,
"My long lost son has returned to me."
   [Open arms widely]

The father ran and showed him his love.
He mimicked the love of the Father above.
The son knelt and cried,
　"I've really hurt you.
I can't be your son.
　Is there work I can do?"
　[Kneel or hang head down]

"I'm just so happy you came back to me.
I thought you were dead,
　but you're alive, I can see.
That which was lost, now is found.
I'll throw you the biggest party around."
　[Raise arms and shake them]

Now don't forget that there were two sons.
The older one came and heard all the fun.
He became very angry
　and started to shout.
"What is this great, big party about?"
　[Place hands on hips]

"He was the one who decided to leave.
I stayed here and worked,
　now I don't believe
you've given him the best of everything.
You're treating him just like a king!"
　[Point and shake finger]

But the father had love enough for two.
And God has love enough for you.
Put yourself in the story,
　which son would you be?
How can you show love for others to see?
　*[Extend arms with index fingers pointing
　upward. Slowly move arms to cross chest]*

"Look at Love - Version One." *The Fruits of Faith*. Wiessner, Colleen Aalsburg and Phyllis Vos Wezeman. Prescott, AZ: Educational Ministries, Inc., 1990. Used by permission.

ZACCHAEUS *Called by Christ*

Luke 19:1-10 ♦ ACTION STORY

Jesus is coming!
   [Cup hands to mouth]

Let's all go see!
   [Hold one hand over eyes and look around]

Zacchaeus was short,
   [Hold hand low to indicate short]

so he climbed a tree!
   [Move hands in climbing motion]

Soon Jesus walked by.
   [Walk in place]

The crowd was so great.
   [Extend arms at sides]

Jesus told Zacchaeus:
   [Place hand over eyes; look up]

"Come down now! Don't wait!
   [Motion come down]

I'm going to come
   [Point to self]

to your house today.
   [Point away from self]

Go home; Get ready!
   [Point in distance]

I'm on my way!"
   [Walk in place]

"Zacchaeus I know
   [Point to head]

all the ways you've sinned.
   [Shake head no]

So believe in God
   [Point up]

and begin again."
   [Extend arm in gesture of invitation]

Zacchaeus was sorry
   [Wipe tears from eyes]

for the wrongs he'd done.
   [Shake head no]

He re-paid his debt
   [Gesture distributing money]

to everyone.
   [Point to many people]

He trusted Jesus
   [Fold hands in prayer]

and made a new start.
   [Shake head yes]

Little Zacchaeus had a
   [Gesture short]

big change of heart!
   [Place hands over heart]

THE WOMAN AT THE WELL
Living New Life

John 4:1-15, 25-30, 39-42 ♦ RHYTHM STORY

Jesus walked along the road to Galilee.
He and the disciples were hot and thirsty.
They entered the country of Samaria;
Usually they avoided that area.

Nearby there stood a well of great renown.
Jesus sat while the others walked to town.
At noon it was the hottest time of day,
surprisingly a woman walked his way.

She came at noon so no one would see,
yet Jesus said, "Please draw a drink for me."
Why would Jesus talk to someone like her?
If she touched that water it wouldn't be pure!

Jesus told her about the gift of God.
Everything he said sounded very odd.
"If only you understood," Jesus said.
"You would have asked me for water instead!"

His offer sounded very good to her.
Those who drank it would never need water.
They would be filled with a bubbling spring.
To never thirst again? What a great thing!

"Please sir, give me that water right away!"
Then Jesus had more he wanted to say.
Jesus talked to her all about her life.
He knew all about her sin and her strife.

She recognized him. God had sent the Son.
This Jesus surely was the Promised One!
The disciples returned with food just then.
Why was Jesus talking to that woman again?

Jesus said, "My water is for everyone.
It doesn't matter what a person has done.
I offer new life to male and female.
I give them the source that will never fail."

The woman left her jar and ran to town.
She spoke to everyone who was around.
As she talked of Jesus the woman glowed.
Out of her, Jesus' living waters flowed.

The people were amazed at what they heard.
They went to find Jesus and listen to His word.
Soon they had what only Jesus can give.
Jesus' living water - now they too would live!

The Flavors of Faith. Wiessner, Colleen Aalsburg and Phyllis Vos Wezeman. Prescott, AZ: Educational Ministries, Inc., 1991. Used by permission.

LAST TO FIRST *Places and Priorities*

Mark 9:33-35 ♦ SYLLABLE STORY

Jesus
once heard
his friends
claim that
each would
be first
in Christ's
Kingdom
someday.

Our Lord
explained
to be
great meant
they must
first choose
last place.

Like them
we must
care for
those who
need us
to show
God's love
on earth.

"Last First." *Pilgrimage: Seeking the Kingdom of God.* Wezeman, Phyllis Vos, Anna L. Liechty, and Judith Harris Chase. Mishawaka, IN: Active Learning Associates, Inc., 1998.

JESUS' TRANSFIGURATION

Teach the Transformation

Luke 9:28-36 ◆ ECHO STORY

Jesus took Peter and James and John **UP ON THE MOUNTAINSIDE.**
    (UP ON THE MOUNTAINSIDE)

As He was praying, Jesus was changed **BEFORE THEIR VERY EYES.**
    (BEFORE THEIR VERY EYES)

His clothing glowed brighter than any light **HIS DISCIPLES HAD EVER SEEN.**
    (HIS DISCIPLES HAD EVER SEEN)

James and the others were quite amazed **BY WHAT WAS HAPPENING.**
    (BY WHAT WAS HAPPENING)

A cloud appeared and they heard a voice **THAT SEEMED TO COME FROM WITHIN.**
    (THAT SEEMED TO COME FROM WITHIN)

The Creator of all the Universe said **"THIS IS MY SON, LISTEN TO HIM!"**
    ("THIS IS MY SON, LISTEN TO HIM!")

Jesus and Peter and James and John **WERE ALL CHANGED ON THAT MOUNTAINSIDE.**
    (WERE ALL CHANGED ON THAT MOUNTAINSIDE)

Jesus found strength for His mission and **HIS FRIENDS LEARNED TO LET GOD GUIDE.**
    [HIS FRIENDS LEARNED TO LET GOD GUIDE)

If we seek to know the Creator **BY LISTENING TO JESUS, THE SON.**
    (BY LISTENING TO JESUS, THE SON)

We will be changed by God's power **TO DISCOVER WHAT WE CAN BECOME.**
    (TO DISCOVER WHAT WE CAN BECOME)

The Flavors of Faith. Wiessner, Colleen Aalsburg and Phyllis Vos Wezeman. Prescott, AZ: Educational Ministries, Inc., 1991. Used by permission.

TEMPLE *Turn the Tables*

Matthew 21:12-17; Mark 11:12-19; Luke 19:45-48 ♦
ECHO STORY

Buy! Buy! Buy!
  [Buy! Buy! Buy!]
Cried the sellers in the temple.

Coo! Coo! Coo!
  [Coo! Coo! Coo!]
Doves for offerings here.

Clunk! Clunk! Clunk!
  [Clunk! Clunk! Clunk!]
Coins dropped in merchant's coffers.

More! More! More!
  [More! More! More!]
Fill them to the brim.

Baa! Baa! Baa!
  [Baa! Baa! Baa!]
Little lambs awaiting slaughter.

Bleat! Bleat! Bleat!
  [Bleat! Bleat! Bleat!]
Goats for sacrifice.

Smell! Smell! Smell!
  [Smell! Smell! Smell!]
Wine and oil and salt for sale here.

Try! Try! Try!
  [Try! Try! Try!]
One sniff and you will buy.

No! No! No!
  [No! No! No!]
This place is a house of worship.

Out! Out! Out!
  [Out! Out! Out!]
Not a den of thieves.

Crash! Crash! Crash!
  [Crash! Crash! Crash!]
Tables of the moneychangers.

Bang! Bang! Bang!
  [Bang! Bang! Bang!]
Overturned today.

Stop! Stop! Stop!
  [Stop! Stop! Stop!]
Do not barter in the Lord's house.

Pause! Pause! Pause!
  [Pause! Pause! Pause!]
Take the time to pray.

Praise! Praise! Praise!
  [Praise! Praise! Praise!]
Worship here and offer your thanks.

Ssh! Ssh! Ssh!
  [Ssh! Ssh! Ssh!]
Let God speak to you.

LOVE *Just like Jesus*

Matthew 22:37-39 ♦ ACTION STORY

Love one another.
But she called me a name.
   [Cup hands to mouth]

Love one another.
But he lost our game.
   [Mime action of bouncing ball or swinging bat]

Love one another.
But she pulled my hair.
   [Mime action of pulling hair]

Love one another.
But he didn't play fair.
   [Shrug shoulders]

Love one another.
But she ate my lunch.
   [Mime action of eating sandwich]

Love one another.
But he threw a punch.
   [Clench fist]

Love one another.
But he told a lie.
   [Shake head no]

Love one another.
Here's the reason why...
   [Extend arms at sides]

Love one another.
Jesus told us to.
   [Point up]

Love one another.
Because I love you!
   [Cross arms over chest]

MARY *Offered Her Ointment*

John 12:1-8 ◆ SYLLABLE STORY

Ma-ry
had some
per-fume
that was
pre-cious,
cost-ly,
spe-cial.

One day
when her
good friend
Je-sus
came to
vi-sit,
she sat
down at
his feet.

Ma-ry
took her
oil and
poured it
on him.

She wiped
it off
with her
own hair.

Pe-ople
thought she
wast-ed
mo-ney.

She showed
her love
for the
Savior
in this
spe-cial
manner.

FOOTWASHING
Served by the Savior
John 13:4-17 ♦ ACTION STORY

Jesus rose from supper,
[Stand up]

tied a towel around his waist,
[Pantomime tying towel around waist]

poured water in a basin,
[Pantomime pouring water from pitcher into bowl]

knelt and washed his helpers' feet.
[Kneel on one knee and pantomime washing someone's feet]

Then Jesus challenged his disciples:
[Stand and gesture with index finger toward others]

"Do as I have done to you.
[Point to self then others]

Live a life of loving service.
[Cross arms over chest]

Follow me in all you do."
[Extend arms in front of body]

"Jesus Serves." *Pilgrimage: Seeking the Kingdom of God.* Wezeman, Phyllis Vos, Anna L. Liechty, and Judith Harris Chase. Mishawaka, IN: Active Learning Associates, Inc., 1998.

HOLY WEEK *Day by Day*

Matthew, Mark, Luke, John ♦ RHYTHM STORY

On Sunday of Holy Week
Jesus came to town
riding on a donkey.
The crowds were all around.

"Hosanna," they all shouted,
"Hosanna to our King."
They waved their palms victoriously.
God's praises they did sing.

On Monday of Holy Week,
when Jesus went to pray,
what he saw in the temple
caused him great dismay.

"This is a house of worship
and not a marketplace.
Get out, you moneychangers!"
He rid it of disgrace.

On Tuesday of Holy Week
Jesus shared God's love.
He told the earthly rulers
that his kingdom was above.

He told stories to the people.
He taught lessons for their life.
He heard the rulers plotting.
The town was filled with strife.

On Wednesday of Holy Week
what did Jesus do?
Did he stay with His disciples?
Did he tell them what He knew?

Did he share the day with loved ones
in a place he often stayed?
Did he spend the day preparing
as he talked with God and prayed?

On Thursday of Holy Week
Jesus gathered with his friends.
He washed their feet and told them
that his life was near its end.

He took bread and wine and blessed it,
gave it to his friends to share.
But Judas, his disciple,
was filled with great despair.

Then Jesus and his close friends
went to a garden spot to pray.
When Jesus found them sleeping
He was filled with great dismay.

As he went to leave the garden
Judas met him with a kiss.
The soldiers grabbed him quickly.
What's the meaning of all this?

They led Jesus to the high priest
where the scribes and elders met.
They tried to find a reason
to put the Lord to death.

On Friday of Holy Week
Jesus Christ was crucified.
The Son of God and Son of Man
hung on a cross and died.

On Saturday of Holy Week
Jesus' body was in a tomb.
His faithful friends and followers
were sad and filled with gloom.

On Sunday of the next week
Jesus' friends found a surprise.
A bright and glorious angel
appeared before their eyes.

"He is not here; he's risen,"
is what the angel said.
"You're looking in the wrong place.
He's living. He's not dead."

HOLY WEEK *Events and Emotions*

Matthew 26:17-28:10; Mark 14:12-16:12;
Luke 22:7-24:12; John 12:20-20:18 ♦
ACTION STORY

When Jesus rode through Jerusalem, the disciples felt **EXCITED**.

> *[Gesture EXCITED through face and body movements]*

When Jesus overthrew the moneychangers in the temple, the disciples felt **PUZZLED**.

> *[Gesture PUZZLED through face and body movements]*

When Jesus celebrated the Passover in the upper room, the disciples felt **HAPPY**.

> *[Gesture HAPPY through face and body movements]*

When Jesus served the Lord's Supper, the disciples felt **HONORED**.

> *[Gesture HONORED through face and body movements]*

When Jesus prayed in the Garden of Gethsemane, the disciples felt **TIRED**.

> *[Gesture TIRED through face and body movements]*

When Judas betrayed Jesus, the disciples felt **SCARED**.

> *[Gesture SCARED through face and body movements]*

When the soldiers arrested Jesus, the disciples felt **ANGRY**.

> *[Gesture ANGRY through face and body movements]*

When Pilate tried Jesus, the disciples felt **CONFUSED**.

> *[Gesture CONFUSED through face and body movements]*

When the soldiers mocked Jesus, the disciples felt **ASHAMED**.

> *[Gesture ASHAMED through face and body movements]*

When Jesus was nailed to the cross, the disciples felt **SAD**.

> *[Gesture SAD through face and body movements]*

When Jesus died, the disciples felt **HOPELESS**.

> *[Gesture HOPELESS through face and body movements]*

When Jesus was buried, the disciples felt **LONELY**.

> *[Gesture LONELY through face and body movements]*

When Jesus was laid in the tomb, the disciples felt **PRAYERFUL**.

> *[Gesture PRAYERFUL through face and body movements]*

When Jesus arose from the dead, the disciples felt **JOYFUL**.

> *[Gesture JOYFUL through face and body movements]*

When the disciples remembered God's great gift of salvation through Jesus, the disciples felt **LOVED**.

> [Gesture LOVED through face and body movements]

JESUS *Risen to Reign*

Matthew 28:1-9 ◆ RHYTHM STORY

Early on Sunday morning
the women went to the tomb
where they had laid dear Jesus.
Their hearts were filled with gloom.

When they approached the garden
they had a big surprise:
A bright and glorious angel
appeared before their eyes.

The women were all frightened;
they didn't know what to do.
The angel told them gladly:
"The Lord has risen for you!

Now go and tell the others.
Spread the news both far and near.
The Lord has risen victorious.
Let your hearts be filled with cheer."

THE DISCIPLES
Commissioned by Christ

Matthew 28:16-20; Mark 16:14-20; John 24:36-53 ♦
RHYTHM STORY

They were gathered on a hillside
on a very special day.
Jesus gave a great commission,
he had special words to say.

"I am going back to heaven,
but there's work on earth to do.
You're my friends and my disciples.
I'm entrusting it to you.

I have power on earth and heaven,
and I'm telling you to go
to people everywhere on earth
My love and care to show.

Teach them all the things I've told you.
Baptize them into the name
of the Father, Son, and Spirit.
"Tell the reason why I came.

Even though I'll be far from you,
lo, I'll always be with you.
And my very special blessing
will be on everything you do."

"Syncopated Story." *Fifty Ways for the Fifty Days.* Wezeman, Phyllis Vos. Prescott, AZ:
Educational Ministries, Inc., 1990.

SUNDAY *Emotions of Easter*

John 20:1-18 ♦ ECHO STORY

When Mary walked to the tomb on Sunday morning, was she **SAD**?

[Repeat the last word and gesture SAD through face and body movements]

When Mary saw that the stone had been rolled away from the tomb, was she **FEARFUL**?

[Repeat the last word and gesture FEARFUL through face and body movements]

When Mary ran to tell Peter and John the news, was she **CONFUSED**?

[Repeat the last word and gesture CONFUSED through face and body movements]

When Mary told the disciples that someone had taken Jesus' body, were they **FRIGHTENED**?

[Repeat the last word and gesture FRIGHTENED through face and body movements]

When Peter and John ran to the tomb, were they **PUZZLED**?

[Repeat the last word and gesture PUZZLED through face and body movements]

When John looked inside the tomb, was he **STARTLED**?

[Repeat the last word and gesture STARTLED through face and body movements]

When Peter went inside the tomb, was he **SHOCKED**?

[Repeat the last word and gesture SHOCKED through face and body movements]

When John walked into the tomb, was he **SURPRISED**?

[Repeat the last word and gesture SURPRISED through face and body movements]

When the disciples returned home, were they **GLOOMY**?

[Repeat the last word and gesture GLOOMY through face and body movements]

When Mary wept outside the tomb, was she **LONELY**?

[Repeat the last word and gesture LONELY through face and body movements]

When Mary stooped to look into the tomb, was she **HOPELESS**?

[Repeat the last word and gesture HOPELESS through face and body movements]

When Mary saw two angels sitting inside the tomb, was she **AMAZED**?

[Repeat the last word and gesture AMAZED through face and body movements]

When the angels asked Mary why she was crying, was she **SORROWFUL**?

[Repeat the last word and gesture SORROWFUL through face and body movements]

When Mary told the angels that someone had taken Jesus' body, was she **SCARED**?

[Repeat the last word and gesture SCARED through face and body movements]

When Mary turned and saw a man standing behind her, was she **STUNNED**?

[Repeat the last word and gesture STUNNED through face and body movements]

When the man asked Mary why she was crying, was she **UPSET**?

[Repeat the last word and gesture UPSET through face and body movements]

When Mary asked the man to tell her where they had taken Jesus' body, was she **FORLORN**?

[Repeat the last word and gesture FORLORN through face and body movements]

When Jesus called Mary by name, was she **HONORED**?

[Repeat the last word and gesture HONORED through face and body movements]

When Mary responded to Jesus with the word Teacher, was she **DEVOTED**?

[Repeat the last word and gesture DEVOTED through face and body movements]

When Jesus told Mary to tell the others that he was alive, was she **JOYFUL**?

[Repeat the last word and gesture JOYFUL through face and body movements]

When Mary replied "I have seen the Lord," was she **ALIVE**?

[Repeat the last word and gesture ALIVE through face and body movements]

When Jesus' followers remembered God's great gift of salvation, were they **LOVED**?

[Repeat the last word and gesture LOVED through face and body movements]

PETER *Feed the Flock*

John 21:1-19 ♦ ACTION STORY

The disciples were confused.
[Scratch head]

They weren't sure what they were supposed to do.
[Shrug shoulders and raise arms in questioning gesture]

So Peter said, "Let's go fishing!"
[Motion with arm to follow]

They fished all night long.
[Cast a fishing line]

But they caught nothing.
[Shake head back and forth]

When the sun came up
[Raise hands together over head]

they saw someone standing on the shore.
[Hold hand over eyes]

"Have you caught any fish?" he called.
[Cup hand at mouth]

"No!" they shouted back!
[Cup other hand to mouth]

"Then drop your net on the other side."
[Pantomime moving net from one side to the other]

They did, and caught 153 fish.
[Hold up one, then five, then three fingers]

Then they knew who was standing on shore!
[Nod head up and down]

It was their friend Jesus!
[Cross arms over chest]

Peter jumped into the lake and waded to shore.
[Make swimming motions]

Jesus was cooking breakfast. *[Sniff]*

He served it to the disciples.
[Pass out food]

After breakfast Jesus and Peter took a walk.
[Walk in place]

Three times Jesus asked
[Hold up three fingers]

"Do you love me, Simon Peter?"
[Point away from body, cross hands over chest, and point to self]

Three times Peter answered
[Hold up three fingers]

"Yes, Lord, you know I do."
[Shake head yes]

And Jesus simply told him
[Extend index finger from mouth to front of body]

"Then feed my sheep." *[Open arms wide]*

ACTS 2 *Awaiting Agape*

Acts 2 ♦ ACTION STORY

The people all gathered - **AWAITING**
   [Look from right to left, hand above eyes, while saying AWAITING]

God's promised gift to - **APPEAR**.
   [Look up on APPEAR]

They prayed with one mind in - **ACCORDANCE**
   [Kneel on left knee on ACCORDANCE, lock arms with another person, and bow head]

And **AGREED** that God's Spirit was near.
   [Nod head on AGREED]

The wind left them all quite - **ASTONISHED**.
   [Sway side to side with amazed expressions on ASTONISHED]

The flames seemed to dance in the - **AIR**.
   [Look up and point in astonishment on AIR]

They arose open-mouthed in - **AMAZEMENT**
   [Rise to a standing position with mouth open and hold hands to each side of face on AMAZEMENT]

And shouted "**ALLELUIA! GOD'S HERE!**"
   [Cup hands to each side of mouth repeating "ALLELUIA! GOD'S HERE!"]

They rushed out the door to - **ASSEMBLE**
   [Run in place on ASSEMBLE]

And announce their good news **ALL AROUND**.
   [Turn in a circle on ALL AROUND]

They spoke without even an - **ACCENT**
   [Shake head no on ACCENT]

And explained how God's love could **ABOUND**.
   [Draw a large heart in the air on ABOUND]

Peter spoke of the Christ, God's **ANOINTED**
   [Sign for Christ on ANOINTED by holding out hands, palms up, and touching each hand to the other in the center of the palm to indicate Christ's wounds]

Who was dead, yet on Easter **AROSE**.
   [Hold arms to the side on DEAD, to indicate the cross, then sweep arms forward, lifting palms toward heaven on AROSE]

And 3,000 chose to **ACCEPT** Him
  [Fold hands together and bring to chest over heart on ACCEPT]

To **ADMIT** they had lived as God's foes.
  [Drop chin to chest in humility on ADMIT]

ASSURED and **WASHED CLEAN** by the Spirit
  [Open arms out wide on ASSURED; then sweep arms forward in one motion crossing them in front of body on WASHED CLEAN, and finally bringing them to each side, palms facing front]

The believers began to **ACCLAIM**
  [Clap palms together on ACCLAIM as though crashing cymbals]

The Good News to **ALL** who would hear it
  [Point in sweeping motion on ALL]

And **AGAPE** was shared in Christ's name.
  [Repeat the sign for Christ, touching each palm, then gesturing out with both palms facing up, as though offering Christ to others on AGAPE]

PENTECOST *Sending the Spirit*

Acts 2 ◆ ACTION STORY

LEADER When God first wanted to create the world, do you know how things got done?

ALL God *[clap hands]*
Sent *[slap thighs]*
The *[clap hands]*
Spirit *[cross hands in front of face, palms facing outward and fingers open and outstretched, while shaking hands as they cross]*
The *[clap hands]*
Ho- *[slap thighs]*
-ly *[clap hands]*
Spirit *[cross hands in front of face, palms facing outward and fingers open and outstretched, while shaking hands as they cross]*

LEADER That's right, and life began. Then human beings lost their way in darkness, do you know how God sent light?

ALL God *[clap hands]*
Sent *[slap thighs]*
The *[clap hands]*
Spirit *[cross hands in front of face, palms facing outward and fingers open and outstretched, while shaking hands as they cross]*
The *[clap hands]*
Ho- *[slap thighs]*
-ly *[clap hands]*
Spirit *[cross hands in front of face, palms facing outward and fingers open and outstretched, while shaking hands as they cross]*

▷

LEADER And the words came out just
right!
But it seemed that most folks
did not get the message,
so God had another plan.

ALL God *[clap hands]*
Sent *[slap thighs]*
The *[clap hands]*
Spirit *[cross hands in front of
face, palms facing outward and
fingers open and outstretched,
while shaking hands as they
cross]*
The *[clap hands]*
Ho- *[slap thighs]*
-ly *[clap hands]*
Spirit *[cross hands in front of
face, palms facing outward and
fingers open and outstretched,
while shaking hands as they
cross]*

LEADER And Jesus came
in the likeness of man.
Then Jesus took on all the sin
and darkness, and death
though it won the day. But…

ALL God *[clap hands]*
Sent *[slap thighs]*
The *[clap hands]*
Spirit *[cross hands in front of
face, palms facing outward and
fingers open and outstretched,
while shaking hands as they
cross]*
The *[clap hands]*
Ho- *[slap thighs]*
-ly *[clap hands]*
Spirit *[cross hands in front of
face, palms facing outward and
fingers open and outstretched,
while shaking hands as they
cross]*

▷

LEADER And the stone was rolled away!
On Pentecost Day,
the faithful gathered
wishing Jesus could still be
there.

ALL God *[clap hands]*
Sent *[slap thighs]*
The *[clap hands]*
Spirit *[cross hands in front of
face, palms facing outward and
fingers open and outstretched,
while shaking hands as they
cross]*
The *[clap hands]*
Ho- *[slap thighs]*
-ly *[clap hands]*
Spirit *[cross hands in front of
face, palms facing outward and
fingers open and outstretched,
while shaking hands as they
cross]*

LEADER And God's power was
everywhere! So to the church
in every age,
God sends the wind and flame.

ALL God *[clap hands]*
Sent *[slap thighs]*
The *[clap hands]*
Spirit *[cross hands in front of
face, palms facing outward and
fingers open and outstretched,
while shaking hands as they
cross]*
The *[clap hands]*
Ho- *[slap thighs]*
-ly *[clap hands]*
Spirit *[cross hands in front of
face, palms facing outward and
fingers open and outstretched,
while shaking hands as they
cross]*

LEADER And we are never the same!

"A – Alleluia." *Pentecost Alphabet.* Wezeman, Phyllis Vos, Editor. Prescott, AZ: Educational Ministries, Inc., 1994. Used by permission.

SAUL TO PAUL
Converted to Christianity
Acts 9:1-31 ◆ RHYTHM STORY

There was a man whose name was Saul.
He hated Christians so.
He tortured and arrested them
wherever he would go.

While traveling down the road one day
there came a brilliant light.
It startled him and made him fall.
His mind was filled with fright.

A voice came out of heaven.
It was no one Saul could see.
Jesus asked an important question:
"Why are you persecuting me?"

When you hurt the ones who love me,
you are hurting me as well.
I would like to change your heart Saul,
so my praises you will tell.

Now go on to Damascus.
A man will meet you there.
Saul's eyes were blind and crusted;
People led him everywhere.

A man named Ananias
trusted God enough to go
to place his hands on Saul and say,
"The Lord's love you will show."

Saul witnessed to many people.
His name was changed to Paul.
He preached and taught and witnessed
that Jesus was Lord of all.

Saul to Paul: Enlightened to Serve. Wiessner, Colleen Aalsburg and Phyllis Vos Wezeman. Prescott, AZ: Educational Ministries, Inc., 1989. Used by permission.

PETER *Power in Prison*

Acts 12:1-19 ◆ ACTION STORY

Peter kept proclaiming the message of Jesus
   [Cup hands to mouth]

until one day the rulers had him arrested and put in prison.
   [Cross wrists to symbolize chains]

But his friends in the Church prayed for him.
   [Fold hands in prayer gesture]

One night as he slept
   [Place both hands on side of face and close eyes]

with prison guards watching him
   [Cup one hand over eyes]

suddenly an angel appeared.
   [Extend arms in gesture of surprise]

Peter's chains fell away.
   [Cross wrists and move arms down]

Peter and the angel walked right past the guards.
   [Walk in place]

In the cool night air
   [Wrap arms around self]

Peter realized he wasn't dreaming.
   [Place hands on cheeks]

Peter walked to the house where his friends met for church.
   [Walk in place]

He knocked and knocked on the door.
   [Knock]

When Rhoda, the servant girl, opened the door
   [Gesture opening door]

she was so surprised she slammed the door and ran away.
   [Slam door and run in place]

Peter knocked again.
   [Knock]

This time all his friends came to see who was at the door.
   [Open door]

Imagine their joy when they realized
   [Cross hands over heart]

Peter was truly free
   [Extend arms wide]

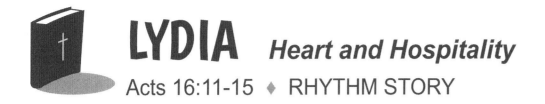

LYDIA *Heart and Hospitality*

Acts 16:11-15 ◆ RHYTHM STORY

Lydia was a merchant,
a seller of purple was she.
She lived in Thyatira
and was prosperous as could be.

On the Sabbath morning
Paul and Silas went to pray.
They were greeted by the women
at the river bank that day.

After Lydia heard Paul's message
her heart was opened to believe.
With her household she was baptized
and the Savior did receive.

She invited Paul and Silas
to her home that very day,
and offered hospitality
to them in many ways.

ABOUT THE AUTHOR

As a religious educator, Phyllis Wezeman has served as Director of Christian Nurture at a downtown congregation in South Bend, Indiana, Executive Director of the Parish Resource Center of Michiana, and Program Coordinator for ecumenical and interfaith organizations in Indiana and Michigan.

In academics, Phyllis has been Adjunct Faculty in the Education Department at Indiana University South Bend and in the Department of Theology at the University of Notre Dame. She is an Honorary Professor of the Saint Petersburg (Russia) State University of Pedagogical Art where she taught methods courses. She has also been guest lecturer at the Shanghai Teachers College in China.

As founder of the not-for-profit Malawi Matters, Inc., she develops and directs HIV & AIDS Education programs with thousands of volunteers in nearly 200 villages in Malawi, Africa including "Creative Methods of HIV & AIDS Education," "Culture & HIV-AIDS," and "Equipping Women/Empowering Girls."

Author or co-author of over 1,950 articles and books, she has written for over 80 publishers.

Phyllis served as President of Active Learning Associates, Inc. and as a consultant or board member to numerous organizations such as the American Bible Society, Church World Service, and the Peace Child Foundation; leader of a youth exchange program to Russia and the Ukraine; and Project Director for four Lilly Worship Renewal grants. She is the recipient of three Distinguished Alumni Awards and recipient of the Aggiornamento Award from the Catholic Library Association.

Wezeman holds undergraduate degrees in Business, Communications, and General Studies and an MS in Education from Indiana University South Bend.

Phyllis and her husband Ken (who met when they were in second and third grade in elementary school) have three children, five grandchildren, and a great-grandson.

phyllis vos wezeman

100 Creative Techniques for Teaching Bible Stories

In this treasure chest of fun ideas and activities, you'll find a wealth of practical possibilities for reviewing Scripture stories with the young and old. These easy-to-use techniques require very simple materials; for some you need only a Bible and your imagination. Each technique can be used for multiple purposes: to teach a prayer, to tell the story of a saint, or to enjoy a Scripture story in a new way. It is an ideal resource for catechists and religion teachers as well as for those preparing liturgies, summer programs, and intergenerational activities.

108 PAGES • 8½"x11" • PW101

Experience the Saints

Activities for Multiple Intelligences

Eight activities per saint, each based on a different learning intelligence. Includes whole family and general classroom guides, with reproducible handouts.

- Vol. 1: Patrick, James, Hildegard of Bingen • PW201
- Vol. 2: Francis, Clare, Margaret of Scotland • PW202
- Vol. 3: Joan of Arc, Thomas Becket, Agnes • PW203
- Vol. 4: Peter, Catherine of Siena, Scholastica • PW204

200 PAGES PER VOLUME • 8½"x11"

Praying by Number
Creative Prayer Lessons & Activities

- Two volumes, with 20 activities each.
- Fun and faith-filled ways to teach children and families how to talk to God.

76 PAGES PER VOLUME • 8½"x11" • PW110 / PW111

Seasons by Step: A Week-by-Week Thematic Approach

Use these creative approaches to explore a theme in-depth over the course of a season through Scripture. Each includes **talking points for children's messages, at-home family activities, artwork** for weekly symbols, and more.

Know Chocolate for Lent *(Lent & Holy Week)*

Uses the growing and manufacturing process of chocolate as a metaphor for the growth of faith and discipleship in the Christian life. Adult formation materials for a parish-wide approach are sold separately. • 80 PAGES • LR119

God's Family Tree *(Lent & Holy Week)*
Tracing the Story of Salvation

Tells the story of God's people as they struggle to find faith and hope for life through the symbols of trees found in Scripture. Includes optional Easter pageant and classroom activities. • 114 PAGES • LR116

In the Name of the Master *(Advent/Christmas/Epiphany)*
Sharing the Story of Christ

Uses a variation of the Advent wreath that uses fruits as symbols for the many names of God's Masterpiece, Jesus. Help your kids & families go deeper as they light their Advent candles each week. • 37 PAGES • LR108

• •

Joy to the World
International Christmas Crafts & Customs

Dozens of activities, from 12 countries that you can use again and again. Develop an appreciation for the contributions of the peoples of all lands and races to the celebration of Christmas. • 159 PAGES • 8½"x11" • LR104

Ideas A-Z
Crafts & Activities for Advent, Christmas, & Epiphany

Offers different theme or learning approach for each letter of the alphabet. Great ideas for intergenerational activities, lesson plans, or worship experiences. • 94 PAGES • 8½"x11" • PW102

Finding Your Way after Your Child Dies

Offers parents a comforting way to grieve. Easily adapted for use in small and large group settings such as a support group, prayer service, or family ministry session. • 192 PAGES • IC937005

http://pastoral.center/phyllis-vos-wezeman

 The Pastoral Center *Pastoral ministers serving pastoral ministers*

Printed in Great Britain
by Amazon